THE GREAT PET SHOP RESCUE

TONY LEE AND GIOVANNI COSTA

EDGE

FRANKLIN WATTS

LONDON·SYDNEY

YOU'RE GOING TO LIKE THIS, **FOSCO**! IT'S THE **GREATEST PLACE IN THE WORLD**!

THE GREATEST PLACE IN THE WORLD IS **BED, DEXTER**. THIS LOOKS LIKE A SHOP.

IT'S FAR MORE THAN THAT! **DOG TREATS** AS FAR AS THE EYE CAN SEE!

OOOH, IT'S BEAUTIFUL!

HELLO BOYS!

MY NAME IS COUNTESS FOSCO.

I'M A **FEMALE PEDIGREE COCKER SPANIEL.** NOT A 'BOY'.

AND 'WOOF' TO YOU TOO!

SAME AS LAST TIME, **JULIE**?

YES, PLEASE. AND ADD SOME MORE TREATS --

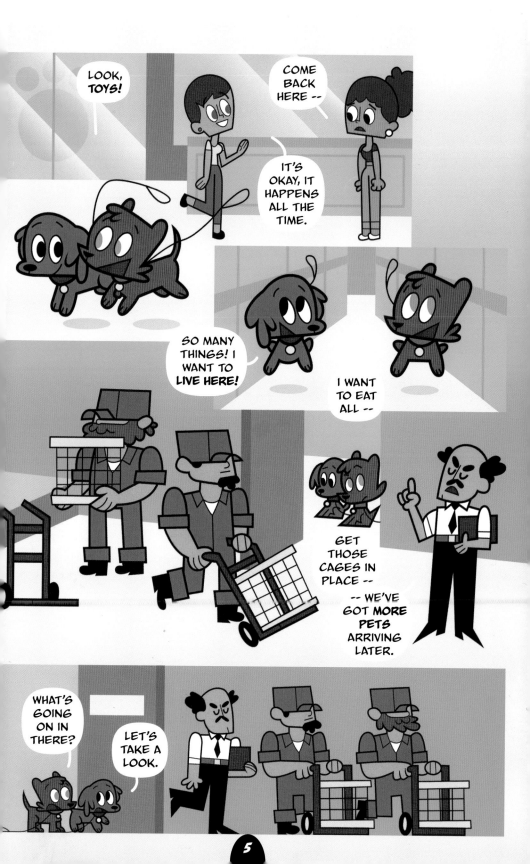

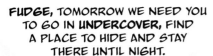

FUDGE, TOMORROW WE NEED YOU TO GO IN **UNDERCOVER**, FIND A PLACE TO HIDE AND STAY THERE UNTIL NIGHT.

WHAT ABOUT THE GUARD DOGS? THEY'RE SCARY!

LEAVE THEM TO US. YOU NEED TO OPEN A DOOR AND LET US IN.

SQUEAKER, YOU'LL NEED TO GET TO THE OFFICE THROUGH THE VENTS.

THAT'S WHERE THE KEYS FOR THE PET HOTEL WILL BE.

I CAN'T DO THAT! I'M TOO **SMALL**!

YOU NEED SOMEONE LIKE A SQUIRREL - FAST AND STRONG!

YOU'RE GOING TO NEED TO OUTSOURCE.

YOU NEED TO TALK TO **MISTER BIG**.

CITY PARK.

SO, HOW DO WE STOP THE HOTEL TAKING MORE PETS?

WE NEED **EVIDENCE.** DEXTER HAS A COLLARCAM, WE'LL RECORD THE BAD CONDITIONS TO PROVE WHAT'S HAPPENING.

WE STILL NEED TO GET PAST THE **GUARD DOGS.** ONE OF THEM'S MAD.

HE THINKS HE'S SOME KIND OF **SUPER-POWERED HERO!** HOW DO WE BEAT THAT?

EASY. WE BECOME **SUPER-POWERED** VILLAINS.

HEY, THEY SAID **THREE CATS** FOR THE HOTEL - BUT THERE ARE **FOUR** HERE.

PROBABLY AN ADMIN ERROR. DON'T WORRY, WE'LL **BILL THEM** FOR FOUR.

COME ON, LET'S GET 'EM TO THE STORE.

SCREECH!

THAT'S ODD! THERE'S **THREE** CATS AGAIN!

DOG FOOD

G FOOD

DOG FOOD

DOG FOOD

DOG FO

STAR BUY!

YOU MUST HAVE COUNTED THEM UP WRONG!

WELL, WE'LL STILL **CHARGE** FOR FOUR ANYWAY!

ALPHA, WHY ARE YOU WEARING THAT MASK?

ALPHA ISN'T HERE. I AM **BAR-KOR**, THE **DEFENDER OF THE DOG BISCUITS.**

OH, RIGHT. SORRY 'BAR-KOR' - I THOUGHT YOU WERE ALPHA --

-- IN A **SILLY MASK** --

-- AGAIN.

BAR-KOR IS HERE TO MAKE SURE THAT BAD PEOPLE DO NOT **STEAL** THE DOG BISCUITS.

BAR-KOR IS A **GOOD BOY.** YES HE IS.

AND I THOUGHT THE DOGS THAT I KNEW WERE MAD.

14

MEANWHILE, AT JULIE'S HOUSE.

THANKS FOR COMING!

THANKS FOR CALLING! MY NEWSPAPER HAS BEEN **INVESTIGATING** ACTIVITY AT HAPIPETZ.

THE MANAGER AT THE PET STORE REALLY DOESN'T SEEM TO LIKE ANIMALS.

YOU'RE RIGHT.

WE'VE ALSO HEARD THAT THEY ARE KEEPING PETS IN THEIR 'HOTEL' **LOCKED IN CAGES.**

FOSCO! WE HAVE A **PROBLEM!**

HENRY KNEW ABOUT THE GUARD DOG BEING A **SUPER HERO.** BUT HE SAID HE'S NEVER BEEN TO **HAPIPETZ!**

I THINK HE'S A **MOLE!**

NO, SQUEAKER - HE'S A **HAMSTER.**

NO - I MEAN A **SPY** FOR HAPIPETZ!

AND HE'S SETTING UP OUR FRIENDS RIGHT NOW!

16

LOOK! THERE ARE THE KEYS TO THE RESTRICTED AREA.

POP!

TAH DAH! A PERFECT LANDING!

AND THE JUDGES AWARD HIM 10 POINTS. DO YOU THINK THE OTHERS ARE OK?

I GUESS.

MR FLUFFYTAIL - I'M SORRY. I CAN'T ALLOW YOU TO LEAVE WITH THOSE KEYS.

WHAT? BUT WE'RE SUPPOSED TO RESCUE THE PETS.

WHY WOULD I DO THAT?

THE MANAGER IS THE ONE WHO CHANGED MY LIFE!

19

-- AND THAT'S WHY I THINK THERE'S SOMETHING STRANGE GOING ON.

PEOPLE SAY THEIR PETS ARE DIFFERENT WHEN THEY COME HOME. PETS ARE GOING MISSING, TOO.

BARK!

BARK!

BUT WITHOUT PROOF AGAINST HAPIPETZ --

BARK!

BARK! BARK!

YES, HAPIPETZ! DO YOU RECOGNISE THE NAME?

WOOF!

HAPIPETZ HOTEL

IT'S ALMOST LIKE SHE'S SAYING 'HAPIPETZ NOW', BUT THE STORE WOULD BE **CLOSED** --

OH! THAT'S IT! SHE WANTS US TO GO TO HAPIPETZ RIGHT NOW!

WAG!

WAG!

HAPIPETZ

WE COULD TAKE DEXTER - HOLD ON, **WHERE IS HE?**

HE HAS A GPS CHIP IN HIS COLLAR --

I DON'T BELIEVE IT!

DEXTER IS IN HAPIPETZ **RIGHT NOW!**

COME ON! THEY'VE **KIDNAPPED** MY DOG!

DO YOU THINK HENRY WILL BE OKAY?

HE'S ALL TIED UP. RIGHT NOW WE NEED TO GET INTO THE RESTRICTED AREA.

PRIVATE
KEEP OUT

LET'S GET THESE PETS OUT OF HERE BEFORE --

-- OH, SERIOUSLY!

SLAM!

OH, LOOK.

TRESPASSERS IN MY STORE.

YOU FOUND OUT MY LITTLE SECRET?

PRETTY SMART FOR DUMB ANIMALS.

HAPIPETZ HOTEL

THIS ISN'T JUST A HOTEL, IT'S A PET FACTORY.

I CHARGE A FORTUNE TO KEEP PEOPLE'S PETS HERE --

AND I CRAM THEM IN, AS MANY AS POSSIBLE!

I'VE GOT SIDELINES IN PUPPY PRODUCTION AND PEDIGREE PET THEFT, TOO.

I HATE ANIMALS. I WAS FORCED TO TAKE OVER HAPIPETZ BY MY FATHER.

AND WHEN I'M DONE, ALL THESE STUPID PETS WILL MAKE ME RICH.

GET HIM!

NO! PLEASE! STOP!

BAD TIME?

DEXTER! EVERYONE! YOU'RE OKAY!

WE THINK HENRY IS --

WORKING FOR THE MANAGER. WE KNOW. THANKS FOR BRINGING THE BACK-UP.

LATER.

WITH THE VIDEO WE FOUND ON THE COLLARCAM,

AND THE EVIDENCE HERE AT THE STORE --

-- HE WON'T BE RUNNING A **PET STORE** FOR QUITE A WHILE.

IT'S ALMOST AS THOUGH THESE PETS HELPED TO CATCH THE MANAGER --

WOOF!

I THINK YOU NEED TO STICK TO **REPORTING**, NOT **FANTASY BOOKS!**

HAH! PROBABLY!

AND ON THAT POINT, I HAVE A **NEWS STORY** TO WRITE.

SEE YOU LATER.

THE END.